MW00931365

Locs for Life:

The Root to Well Being for African-American Women

Kalimah Johnson, LMSW, ACSW

AuthorHouse™
1663 Liberty Drive, Suite 200
Bloomington, IN 47403
www.authorhouse.com
Phone: 1-800-839-8640

First published by AuthorHouse   6/16/2008

Printed in the United States of America
Bloomington, Indiana
This book is printed on acid-free paper.
ISBN: 978-1-4343-5721-2 (sc)

Library of Congress Control Number: 2007910168

Contents

Chapter Four 46

Stages of Locks & The Well Being Connection

Chapter Five 55

Healing for your Hair and Overall Well-Being

Chapter Six 63

Poetry and Pictures

Chapter Seven 109

Common Language

DEDICATION

For Camille, Jordan and Lauren may you always be proud of what God gave you. For my Mama–Geraldine Sheria Turner, I will always be influenced by your upbringing and forever grateful for your love and guidance. I will miss you always…until we meet again

Acknowledgements

I thank God for being constant and ever present in my life and granting every prayer I have ever had and loving me just as I am. I am thankful and humbled by my blessings. It is imperative that I acknowledge and thank my ancestors for their tenacity and will to live, create and survive. My ancestors' endured great pain and suffering but found a way to pass on to my future generation the concepts of love, respect and honor. My ancestors' survival gave me the will to carry on traditions and a commitment to embrace our culture. I am grateful for my partner in life, Keisha Johnson-Price for supporting me in all my endeavors. I thank Keisha for her unconditional love, patience and understanding. I wrote the majority of this book on the train to and from Detroit and Chicago while we shared our first years in marital bliss…in two separate cities… whew! I am very glad for my family and in particular my two sister's Valerie and Teresa who allowed me to play/experiment and finally create in their naturally beautiful hair…I love them dearly.

I'd like to thank a few of my very close friends who have encouraged and inspired me on too many levels to list here. The Detroit/Chicago Poetry Community, Meetery Eatery, The Java Exchange Café, and the Detroit Symphony Orchestra for being creative with me and helping make a dream come true and providing awesome spaces for local and national performance poets to help build the PicNap Poetry Series Brand. Kim Jones, Kendra Ventour, Dr. Janice Fields, Crystal Trammell, Stefanie Fields Bradley, Felicia Williams (Flo's), Pam Taylor, Sonya and Jerry Brown, Dee and Emery, John Maxey (and family), Alia Moss and her book club for serving as my focus group, Dr. Teri Varner, Dr. Kofi Adoma and Reverend Hattie Alexander-Robinson, and the Honorable Judge B. Pennie Millender for all your well wishes and support.

I'd like to thank Sheila Everette-Hale of Cornrows and Braiding Academy-Detroit, Sharon Pryor of Tulani Rose-Detroit, Nefertitti of Textures-Detroit, Tracy and Joyce of Soul Salon Spa-Chicago, Talihah Waajid of Braids Weaves and Things-Atlanta, Derrick Scurry and Thando Kafele-the best lock stylist I know from Brooklyn, New York. The industry would be nothing without you. I am thankful to each of you for mentoring me, challenging me, checking me and seeing me through. It is your shoulders I stand on and I am glad that you have spent your valuable time and creativity towards building and nurturing the foundation of providing comprehensive natural hair care services to clients who desire to wear their hair…as it is.

I'd also like to thank AuthorHouse for giving writers an option to self-publish with a professional polished look. Inohs Sivad, you always save the day, thanks for the book cover design and for re-inventing my image in the media form. I would also like to thank Kerronce Sims who created the illustrations for the lock stages and created my logo for the PicNap™ brand. James Ambrose, thank you for making us all beautiful. I also thank those of you who have taken the chance to go on this journey of locking your hair and using this book as a guide. May this book give you the inspiration and information you need to have an awesome experience with locking your hair and/or sharing this information with those you love.

Peace and Blessings,

Kalimah "LocMama" Johnson

Note: As a reader you may have noticed that on the cover and in the title of this book I spell the word "locs" to describe this hairstyle. Meanwhile, I have spelled the same word "locks" within the text. They are both correct, however when I am using the term in a title or in the possessive form I tend to spell it without the "k". In formal writing or within the text I usually spell it with the "k". I use my discretion and/or mood to determine how I spell it on any given occasion and encourage you to do the same, or at least understand my explanation as to why you will see it spelled both ways. The word spelled "locs" is typically used when I speak of the actual hairstyle. The word "locks" is used when I refer to technique and throughout the text. Again either spelling is acceptable for this body of writing.

Introduction

My Lock Journey

As I look back on how events took place in my journey to locks I have to say that I never thought that this would be an option for me even as I provided lock services to many clients. I was born in the late sixties black power movement to a mother who would consider herself a proud black woman. She took great pride in her blackness, believed to be beautiful and was the lighter skinned among her only female sibling. As a child I overheard conversations between her and my aunt about how my mother would "get away" with things, avoid well deserved spankings or punishment and be treated more fairly because she was the lighter of the two. They would laugh about it but it would hurt me to hear such things and it was obvious that my mother married the darkest man she could find so that her babies would be "black". I remember very early on lessons she taught my sisters and I. She taught us not to judge folks based on skin color, we couldn't even name call in the neighborhood among our peers and use terms such as "blackie", "darkie", "yella" or any other kind of descriptive based on shade or hues shared among black folks.

My mother did not let us have perms...at all. We could barely get our hair pressed unless it was Easter Sunday,

Christmas or some other major event that would bring our families together and to prevent the ridicule of our family and friends and especially our cousins, she would have our hair straightened out. I remember one time an older cousin wanted to take us on a boat trip to an amusement park and refused to do so unless our mother let her press our hair. I did not mind because I recall all the compliments we would get and "oooh, ya'll so pretty when ya'll mama let ya'll get all fixed up" comments we would get along the way. But this time was a little different, my big sister was first to get her hair pressed and my cousin was really good at it, made it look like a fresh perm...old school pressing. However, during the press session my cousin was fanning the hot comb to cool it off before she placed it into her head and "smack!" she made a mistake and slapped my sister in the face with the comb and burned her so bad that her dad came over and cursed our cousin out, told her that she did that because she was jealous of my sister.

I don't believe my cousin or my sisters' dad ever got along after that. I can't remember them ever being kind to each other up until his death. With some cocoa butter and love my sister healed well and has no evidence of this incident today. Well, when it was my turn, I remember my mother standing over our cousin with black magic grease from the freezer and saying to her "...be careful, you know her hair is shorter and tighter than her sisters' and if you burn her she will curse you out and I hate to hear this one cursing like she grown...it breaks my heart."

My Mother

Me

As a child I have to say that I actually liked my hair nappy. What I didn't like were the folks (kids and grown-ups too) that teased me, and the hurtful comments that were made about my hair. I didn't like the standard of what black girls hair was supposed to look like and definitely did not like the way my mother styled my hair. It was too plain, and definitely not like the other girls hair in my school and I just didn't like the way she did it (God bless her though, because when she did my hair I felt the love). As a matter of fact, the only time I ever felt comfortable in my own hair was during African Liberation Day celebrations my mother would take us to yearly in June (also known as "Juneteenth") to remember those slaves in Texas who were not freed until a few years after slavery had been abolished. At those events I would fit in and felt good about my hair. Hardly any of my friends understood liberation on any level, so I would come home from those events and try to tell them but they would tease me. I felt sorry for them because deep down I knew that they just hated themselves (not their fault) and their parents did not attempt to show them how beautiful they were…as is.

In the summer of 1975, I stood in the mirror and parted my hair in very small sections and placed colorful rubber bands on each section, trying to style my own hair and making it impossible to take out so they had to be cut out. I was about seven years old when that happened and I remember my mother being very upset about that. Also, as a child I remember looking forward to getting new dolls so that I could cornrow, braid, twist, and put a whole bag of colorful rubber bands in their hair without the worry of getting in trouble. Instead of playing with dolls in the traditional sense I was only concerned with styling the hair, unlike my big sister (three years older than me) who would create this whole other world with dolls and make up all these mini drama's and life events with her dolls which was wonderful now that I think about it with an adult mind. However, it was clear that my role in this doll drama was to do their hair. Even upon request we could not get white dolls but somehow a few would get in the mix and it did not matter. Those white dolls still got their hair braided neatly with the colorful rubber bands even before the infamous movie Ten with Bo Derek that supposedly made extensions popular among black women. I shrug at the thought that it took a white woman to wear braids with ornaments to make more sisters want their hair like that. Back then I was too young to analyze that level of internalized hate towards ourselves, nor was I able to understand how this hatred is not our fault entirely.

Braiding the dolls and my sisters' hair was good enough to keep me busy. Until one day I was on my porch in the projects hooking up one of my sisters' dolls and a neighbor named Ms. Lovie was walking down the sidewalk with her five year old daughter named Dee and said to me, "You doing that baby dolls' head real good, can you do my baby's hair like that?" I said "bring her here" in my "been here before" tone of voice my family says I have had since I was born. I touched this girls' hair and it felt like cotton and it was springy and curly. It did not feel like the stuff the doll manufacturers try to pass as black hair on the baby dolls. It felt good in my little fingers and I said, "I can do her hair right now." I was excited, but the girls' mother wanted to do it that next Sunday before her first day of school. We agreed and I practiced on anything that looked like hair anticipating my first chance to braid someone's hair that was not my sister or her dramatic dolls. That early Sunday evening we set up on the porch. I had my Blue Magic grease, a comb, some rubber bands, and some of my own colorful barrettes and I created my first masterpiece (in my kid's mind for sure). Once done I was so proud of myself and when Ms. Lovie came back to pick her child up she was very pleased, so pleased that before she left she called my mother outside to see and I remember watching her baby smile and twist and turn so we could view all angles of her cornrows. Ms. Lovie went in her bra and paid me three dollars and asked if I wanted to do this every other week. I looked at my mama for approval and she smiled so big that I just turned to the lady said, "Yeah, then I can have my own money cause sometimes my mama don't be having none!" They all agreed so Dee and I worked it out until my little sister came along a few years later. Dee and her mom Ms. Lovie moved out the neighborhood and I would only do her hair once in awhile when they came to visit her grandfather. This turned out to be a good thing because all I ever used that money for was candy and to help buy my big sister more dolls.

I could not wait for my little sister to be born. We knew she was going to be a girl and all I could think about was braiding her hair. It was October 1979 and only three months later, I remember my mother saying, "Girl, watch her damn soft spot, she too young for all that braiding hair right now!" I would take my time and be very careful, but my little sister was a sweet natured baby and was a good candidate for hair braiding. I know my sisters were glad to have me around because we could not get our hair pressed unless on special occasions so I had plenty of chances to get fly with it. Cornrows every which way, twists, individual braids, plaits, you name it! Then in the summer of 1982, my big sister's father came by with a lady from California doing some kind of extension braids and he wanted my sister to have them. My mother said my little sister and I were too young to get them at that time. When she finished, my big sister's long hair was beautiful and LONGER! I wanted them immediately! I begged for weeks and finally my mother called the lady and she did the same thing for me. I had long hair now! I went outside to swing it in front of my friends. I remember that one of my so-called friends laughed and talked about my new extension braids so bad (and because everybody was easily influenced by her because she was closer to the then white standard of beauty, thereby going along with her teasing) that I went home and cut them out...I mean took them braids down! My mother was furious, and you know I had to hear about how much they charge for extension braids. I was sad that I hurt my mother and when I went back outside without the long braids, guess who was the gladdest? That so-called friend of mine! Then I realized that she just did not want me to have longer hair than her. The lessons we learn about beauty standards. By the way I am still taking care of my sisters' hair today. My big sister has Sisterlocks™ and my little sister wears her hair in an Afro or however she pleases but is still chemical free!

When I was twelve years old (Summer, 1981) I was at a girlfriend's house and we were in the kitchen playing spades listening to the Jackson Five and drinking grape Kool-Aid. A grown man who was there, visiting her mother, came into the kitchen and started in on my hair. At the time it was in an Afro that was cut by Mr. Roosevelt Pickett who lived down the street from me, had all boys, and knew how to cut hair. Usually, his wife would press my hair out of sympathy and against my mother's wishes. But something must have happened and I couldn't get it pressed so her husband gave me this boxer Ali look about the head with his clippers. This man at my friend's house started calling me a boy and saying that I would never get a boyfriend looking like that and so on. Even as a young girl I had a slight problem with my mouth and I knew how to talk like grown folks do, so I started talking about him from head to toe and everybody in the kitchen was cracking up laughing. While I am steadily lighting into him and making him feel real little, he had a rifle's bullet in his hand. He opened the bullet and poured the gunshot pellets into my afro!

Well needless to say, my coils of tightly curled hair i.e. nappy hair held on to the pellets and they would not roll out. He then said, "Take some of these bb's to match the bb's in your hair." What was a funny situation at the time turned out of control, my girlfriends was dying laughing by now with a comb trying to get the bb's out, the teeth in the comb were breaking and buckshots were flying across the room and folks were ducking and saying that my naps were shooting them and bb's were hitting the cabinets and dishes in the sink and it was just ridiculous! I started crying and that was the first time I ever thought that I hated my hair.

Well my big sisters' grandfather used give us ten dollars a month for allowance and when the first of the month came around I was right there with my girlfriend Linda (who helped pull the bb's out of my hair) waiting on that allowance then we walked straight to the corner store and purchased my first box of Dark & Lovely™ (or it may have been Gentle Treatment™) hair permanent for $3.99. Yeah this was in the early eighties so the box perm was pretty cheap! Linda's big sister Marci put it in and I waited for the compliments to roll in like they would when I would get my hair pressed on special days and the compliments did come. Especially from Linda's brothers whom one of them I had a crush on anyway, so I felt beautiful and validated…until I got home. My mother almost cried. I did not grow to understand her hurt until now. Not until I wore my hair out, tore my hair out, and ignored my hair for many years did I understand the nappy seed she tried to plant from birth in all of us.

Once I became a young adult I decided that extension braids were the best choice for me. Braids were my answer to wanting long and acceptable hair; they were virtually low maintenance and kept up with my busy lifestyle. The braided bob with burnt ends, which cropped my face beautifully, got me through college and grad school. Braiding hair also got me through financially. For the most part, I braided hair at home and still took care of my sisters' and mother's hair. Doing extensions were exhaustive, but nonetheless a wonderful way to stay connected to my women friends/family during this busy time…we bonded this way. We had a chance to catch up with our lives and some of the deepest most revealing conversations I have ever had has been with sisters while doing their hair or getting my hair done. While now all I do is locks, the exchange of stories, love sharing, and positive energy is the same. What's more beautiful though is the possibility of showing someone that the hair that they were born with, the hair that has been hidden for so long due to a plethora of reasons, will now be revealed, revered, nurtured, and shown to the world; and will show beautifully!

While attending Wayne State University in the 90's I decided to pursue a bachelors and masters degree in Social Work. I thought I should formalize what I already knew was deep within me, which is the passion to help people. More specifically, raising the consciousness of black women and increasing their understanding of whom they are and a celebration of that through acceptance, recognizing their beauty and promoting personal inner peace. Considering that black women have been impacted by many ills of society including slavery, racism, rape, domestic violence, incest, and economic disparities to name a few, this task at hand is great. I started making the connection to healing through locking our hair during a research project I was doing on African-American father-daughter relationships while completing a requirement set forth by a scholarship program I was in. I validated this "lock your hair for well- being" idea not by numbers or questionnaires as one would think but through an interaction with a woman who changed my life. Joy Royes was a grad student in Psychology originally from New York who was assigned to help me with analyzing data that I had collected for my study, and through this mentoring relationship I learned about this idea that black women can lock their hair as an option to help them heal from the old standards and still be beautiful.

When I met Joy she had this, what I call a Detroit hairdo. Detroit hair stylists have always been very talented and sometimes to their own demise. I swear she had a wrap on one side, pump waves on the other side, a ponytail in the back, and a rainbow of hair spray paint to boot! This entire getup was going on in one head...no joke! I never said anything about it, I've had enough hair issues to just meet her where she was and celebrate her unique expression of beauty. However, I thought to myself, "Who would take her serious in a PhD program with her hair looking like that?" I digress. Anyway, one day she said to me, "I don't want my hair like this anymore, I am going through some things" and I said, "Well, what are you going to do with it now?" Afraid of what she might say, but clueless nonetheless. She said, "I am going to lock it up." "Dreads?" I said. She went on to say yes, and explained that she preferred to call them locks because there is nothing dreadful about our natural hair. I listened to her and then I wanted to know who in the hell does dreads, oops I mean locks, in Detroit. I asked her and she stated that she would go home to Brooklyn and have them done by a friend, his name is Thando Kafele. My next question was how was she going to be able to afford going back and forth to have them maintained and her response was easy and convenient. That's right, I would have to cultivate them and she was going to show me how to do them like Kefele. Then she said, "You already know how to braid, it will be simple."

I was reluctant, but agreeable. I already thought she was brilliant and looked forward to the opportunity to spend time with her and pick her brain about statistics and research. When she first came back to Detroit after having her locks done I was amazed to say the least. I couldn't wait for her to explain to me how he did it. She said he did it with a comb and twirled the comb through her natural hair creating these coils, which shocked me because she already had long hair, but it had perm in it and all that straight hair was cut off to start her locks, so her hair was very short now. I gained a new kind of respect for her just watching her go through the process of locking her hair in this traditional way. I followed the instructions she gave me and fell in love with the process. In the meantime, she was still looking for a professional to cultivate her locks. She found someone by the name of Iman and told me that they were also looking for braiders and the Christmas break was coming, so I worked in her shop during that short time. What I learned there was invaluable. I realized my worth, skill, and talent for styling natural hair. I also learned that I had the capacity to cultivate locks. So when school started back in January, the money I saved for my books for the winter semester I spent with Nkinge at the Shrine of the Black Madonna Bookstore in Detroit. Social Work books would have to wait because I bought all natural hair care books with my earnings. Then I went on a mission to find a natural stylist who could mentor me. I found two: Sheila Everette-Hale of Everettes Natural

Hair and Braiding Academy and Sister Nefertitti of Textures Salon both of Detroit. These sisters did not know me from Eve, but helped me via telephone for years to come. By the time we met each other in person they had already established and received me as a colleague and I am honored to be among them still.

So there I was locking folk's hair by the packs, still no locks for myself. Knowing everything there is to know about hair locking, still no locks for myself. Using my group processing skills learned while earning a masters degree and the experience I gained in the working world as a therapist for abused and neglected women and children, still no locks for myself. Holding what I call PicNap™ gatherings in my sister's home for my hair clients who needed emotional support, information, guidance, and encouragement for wearing their hair in locks, still no locks for me. Then finally at one of these gatherings, my clients decided that they would challenge me, love on me, and explain to me that I need to practice what I preach, by locking my own hair and reluctantly…I agreed.

It was April 6, 2001 that I started my journey of locking my hair. Approximately 7 years after I had become "LocMama" for many. In locking my own hair I have learned about the connection one feels with a complete stranger who also has locks and you give them that supportive nod. I began to use my time in the morning getting ready for the world, which did not include a fight or fussing with my hair. I began to learn what it feels like to go on vacation, get my hair wet, and a hair emergency does not immediately follow. But most importantly, I began to understand that total acceptance of myself is healing and essential to my personal well-being. Honoring the way God made my hair, using a talent that it appears I was born with, honoring our ancestors, freeing myself from expectations that don't fit me, and loving myself with my hair "as it is" was the lesson learned. And even with the way I was raised by my proud mother, having an early understanding of my self-worth, valuing my culture and loving my hair, there were still some internal struggles concerning black beauty and nappy hair that I had to deal with.

Therefore, through my own personal and professional experiences and with great contemplation, thought, and deep exploration, I am proposing that black women can heal from past beauty standards that cause emotional stress and trauma (recognizing that some medical and/or external situations can prevent some women from locking their hair) which has impacted their self-esteem, self-worth, and value as well as exceptionality. Moreover, I am proposing that women can recover from the aforementioned by locking their hair as one of many options towards overall well-being. Also, this book has been written for those sisters that I know are out there and want to lock their hair but are just too afraid to start. This book is also for sisters who have already started the journey to locking and need some encouragement along the way. It will also be useful for professional lock stylists, locticians, lock mama's, lock daddy's, lock cultivists, culturists, and all the other names that may be out there to describe the liberating, mind freeing, healing and creative work we do.

I have learned and gained specialized knowledge through freeing folks from that need to have straight, long and shiny hair. A paradigm shift has to occur and it is my hope that my story will help you get there. I have learned that our hair can be healthy, strong, glowing, beautiful and long (or short if this is what you like). My journey has also taught me lessons in healing as well as taken me on a spiritual journey that no black woman should be ignorant of. And even if this book does not help you take the leap and lock your hair, at least it will serve as a testimony to those of us who have. Our journey's are not nor will they ever be the same, but my goal was to speak on the commonalities and benefits of wearing your hair locked, and to celebrate the ultimate expression of acceptance of self as a way of life.

Why Another Natural Hair Care Book?

After looking at the literature and reviewing what is already on the market regarding natural hair I have come to several conclusions. First, there are several books available on the market, however when considering the rate to which folks are going natural there aren't nearly enough. Second, most of the books reviewed covered a variety of options towards wearing your natural hair and even fewer of these books specifically or exclusively discussed locks. In addition, while some of the books had chapters on locking and discussed in some detail the transition one must go through to lock the hair, an element that has gotten less attention is the notion that hair locking can be an option for one to increase their overall well-being.

In particular, black women have had to conquer many issues regarding beauty standards, image and self-esteem. We have healing to do in ways that only we can speak on and in this book, I am proposing that some of this healing work has been done in the process of getting our hair locked and wearing our hair out in the world "as is."

As the title indicates, this book is for women who have thought about locking their hair, but just too afraid to do so; and for women who already know and understand the beauty and advantages of locking, and getting to the root of it all by having a close and personal discussion about how to do it. Therefore, to sisters who are thinking about locking your hair use this book as a means of information, encouragement, and guidance. To women who already have locks, use this book as reinforcement, validation, and understanding.

My goal is to put into words the examples of how black women have healed and liberated themselves by deciding to lock and living through the stages as well as coping with the comments (good and bad) from their partners, family members, friends and in their work environments. The most important component is sharing with you everything there is to know about locking your hair and how to live with locks in the most healthy, honorable and adoring way.

The Well Being/Cultural Connection

As a loctician I have had the honor of cultivating hundreds of women's crowns into beautiful locks. Some women have only visited with me once, to get the locks started and to have someone consult with them on how to care for and maintain the locks as they grow. Some women have come to me and I have been their primary hair care professional throughout their entire locking experience and beyond. The person and provider relationship is where great things happen. The client seeking services and the professional providing the services have very distinctive roles in the process of growing locks and it is the interaction between the two that will determine how this experience will be for both of them. I am not proposing that in order to lock your hair you have to consult with a professional because with guidance and appropriate information you can cultivate and grow beautiful locks on your own. However, when starting it is a good idea to have a loctician at the very least consult with you. Many experts and writers on this topic have suggested that one should at least start off their new locks with a loctician. Even I had help with starting my locks. Melanie, owner of Knappy Heads started my locks, even after I had been cultivating and growing beautiful locks for others for several years. I deal with each client using a holistic approach and sometimes, potential customers who have been burned (pun intended) by the hair/beauty industry find this refreshing. I also use the "person in environment" technique to get a better understanding of environmental factors as well as past events, which may have already impacted a potential client in terms of how they view themselves, their natural hair, and where they are with wearing their hair "as is" also known as nappy.

As a Social Worker one of the basic most obvious connections I could make as to why so many sisters have locked their hair and report loving the experience is evidenced in the four core values in helping individual's live free, happy and liberated lives. These four core values are outlined in the National Association of Social Workers Code of Ethics and are as follows:

1. *Respecting the Dignity and Worth of all Individuals*
2. *Promoting Self-Determination*
3. *Honoring an Individual's Choice and course of action-as long as it is Safe*
4. *Providing Competent Comprehensive Services to Clients*

With these four core values in place it is no wonder that folks who have locked their hair enjoy it so much. It validates who they are and it works with them where they are at, instead of making them do something that the hair would not naturally do. Deciding to lock is liberating because it is your right to choose and it feels awfully good when you have placed your hair into the hands of someone that can articulate what you want and knows what he or she is doing and is passionate about doing so.

Also, from an afrocentric perspective, cultivating and wearing locks are like practicing the principles of Kwanzaa.

Umoja means unity, locked hair can be an expression of you becoming one with yourself and the community, embracing your heritage and showing it by celebrating your happy to be nappy crown of locks.

Kujichagulia means self-determination, where you identify and name yourself and decide and embrace your locks as what is beautiful, instead of having others identify that for you.

Ujima means collective work and responsibility, by wearing your locks to work or while doing business reveals the fact that you expect to be treated respectfully and may encourage others to do the same and hopefully at the same time dispelling myths about folks who have locked hair.

Ujamaa means cooperative economics and having a natural hair care provider service you from time to time or on a regular basis can keep our hard earned dollars in our communities. Better yet, there is a listing of African American folks on the reference page who have written extensively on locking hair as well as provide services; visit with them, support them and purchase their books, products and adornments to keep this principle alive and well.

Nia means purpose and while I have heard some very interesting reasons for why some lock their hair, the explanations that revealed that locks are more than just a hairstyle are the ones that stick with me. For instance, a woman told me that she did not know that locking her hair would free up her mornings for prayer, meditation and reflection instead of doing her hair, now her locks have served a purpose in her journey towards a fuller and better relationship with a higher power of her own understanding. What could be more purposeful?

Kuumba means creativity and I have witnessed many testimonials to women who have locked to become more creative and I have also had a chance to really get creative with lock styling in my efforts to "unlock" the potential of nappy hair.

Imani means faith and to grow locks from the beginning stages to mature locks one will have to believe that beauty is possible with nappy hair. If the individual does not have faith, going through the phases where the locks aren't looking like a person would want them to will certainly teach a lesson or two on patience and faith.

Well-being can be evidenced by how well a person is adjusted to their environments and how good they feel among others and most importantly how positive they feel about showing their true selves to the world. Locking your hair can put you right in the middle of the aforementioned and having a competent, comprehensive, knowledgeable and caring loctician on your side and in your corner can get you through this wonderful yet challenging process.

The Real Deal on Nappy Hair

Anatomy of African-American Hair

When I first started cultivating locks I had so much to learn about our natural hair. I started reading up on and studying the teachings of pioneers like Nekhena Evans, Pamela Ferrell, Tulani Kinard, Diane Bailey, Dr. JoAnne Cornwell, Sheila Everette-Hale and others. Based on their teachings it is always good to know the structure and science behind the make up of our hair. I will not get too scientific, but I will describe to you in simple fashion the anatomy of black hair. Our hair strands are anchored by what is called a follicle. The follicle is comprised of the medulla, cortex and cuticle. The follicle is rooted inside of the papilla and is also present with the sebaceous gland. This gland is responsible for the amount of sebum (or natural oil) that coats your hair naturally. This is a very simplistic way of describing the structure, however if you need an illustration and more detail the best reads for this would be the book No Lye by Kinard or the book Everything you Need to Know about Hairlocking by Evans, they explain it very well…for real.

The next topic I'd like to discuss is our hair texture(s). I have learned a great deal about the many textures of our hair through cultivating locks for many women with different and varying types. I like to describe hair in terms of fabric because it gives me a better and simpler way of explaining to clients without it getting too personal if you know what I mean. Hair texture has been a very sensitive topic for many black women because of the way we were raised and how we were negatively impacted by the many images of our hair textures in mass media. Overall, I know that some of us have been hurt and are in need of some healing to cope with this. I have decided not to include images that were hurtful to us concerning our hair but if you would like to see these images go to: http://www.ferris. edu/jimcrow/picaninny/

In initial conversations with sisters who are interested in getting their hair locked the first thing I tell them is that black women can have up to nine different combinations of hair textures, not just nappy or curly or straight or good or bad. Our hair has a certain thickness, pliability, and capacity to handle water when wet which determines the texture. So I ask, "When your natural hair gets wet does it hold water or does the water roll off with ease?" "Does your hair feel like cotton, silk or wool?" "When you look at a strand that has come out, does it lay flat on a flat surface, or does it rise and fall with lots of dents in between?" "How many curves can you count on one strand?" is another question I might ask, just to get them thinking about what kind of hair they might have before our visit. Some clients who have chemically processed their hair don't have a clue about the texture of their hair, and that's when we have to get them to grow out the chemical to some degree in order to find out. A very interesting conversation will take place indeed. Then I tell them the possibilities of all those hair types and the projected outcome of starting locks. If your texture is in the cotton family and curves more, your chances of locking are at best. If your hair is in the wooly family and have more to some curves your chances of locking will be good too. If your hair belongs to the silky clan then you may face some difficulty with locking and will have to prepare yourself for the even longer road ahead.

Some not so reputable locticians will decline helping individuals with "so-called" hard to lock hair and I personally would not do that because if that person really wants locks we should be proficient enough to know how to get them there, and also have pictures of mature locks available to the client to review for an idea of what their locks may look like in the future. Even non-black folks want locks for many different reasons and I take the position that each individual has his or her own journey and if locks is a part of that journey, so be it. I also don't disrespect the natty dread and/or the commonly termed dreadlocks. Dreadlocks are more commonly worn among folks who practice Rastafarianism. I also consider them the originators to this now fashionable movement towards wearing locks. If not for Rastafarians, what would we Africans in America know about locks?

I also honor locks that have occurred because of circumstance. I have seen locks on the homeless population and thank God for them. I also attempt to teach my clients to have the same attitude towards locks because if we get into what would be considered "nice dreads" or "neat locks" is that any different from the mentality of "good" versus "bad" hair or "cheap" versus "expensive" locks? We all like clean locks, but some of the less fortunate individuals that survive in our communities don't have that option. So, pray for them, volunteer, use your energy towards helping the less fortunate, and by all means honor each individual's right to choose and wear their locks for themselves. I certainly believe that locks are one in the same, and to teach mutual respect of "all kinds of dreads" is to honor that locks come in many forms and fashions. It's only fair, and it validates that each person is worthy and gives them options, instead of hurting their feelings because of texture, type, and style (or lack thereof). Although I provide services to those who want a more groomed and stylized version of locks, that does not mean that any other expression of locks is inappropriate or undesirable.

Professionals need to realize that more than likely a change in how one has experienced their hair and what they think about it is actively going on during the initial consultation. For instance, most black folks have told family members with silky or wavy hair textures that they have "good" hair (and so on) for all of their lives. Now they want locks and figure that it must be "good" for that too and to be told by a professional that their hair is not "good" enough is mean spirited and I challenge locticians to develop a way to explain their options without hurting folks who are starting the journey. The wavy headed or "good haired" people that want locks are certainly not going to stop with one consultation and believe me, if the next stylist asks the right questions, the client will tell on the last consultant and how they were pushed out of the shop by those who don't do so-called "good" hair types. It's almost as if some folks and some locticians (very few, but you know how a few apples can spoil the bunch) that provide services to those with nappy kinky hair are so happy that now nappy hair is "good" for locking, that they want to keep it for themselves, instead of sharing this new found freedom from chemicals and wearing locks with those whose hair might present a challenge. One certain way to gain a sense of well-being and personal healing is to accept people as they are and work with them in the spirit of love. Recognizing that our beauty lies in the simple fact that we come in all shades, hues, and hair textures is key to recovering from past pain, which has separated us for years dating back to slavery in this country.

Locks- The Evolution towards the Expression of Total Acceptance of Self

The Highest Expression of Acceptance of Self

When we were captured in Africa and brought here to America, we didn't have the option to pack our belongings. We were kept from utilizing our traditions and language. Also left behind was our understanding of how to care for our hair. We were beaten into submission, raped, hung and even killed for trying to be anything other than a submissive slave. After years of this treatment, along with dealing with the Willie Lynch legacy, Jim Crow, segregation, racism and oppression we learned to absolutely hate ourselves. Our self-hatred became so normalized that we sometimes don't recognize when we hate on each other. One expression of self hatred and denial of who we really are is the notion that the closer you look to white the better off you are and the efforts we put forth to look as close to white as possible has impacted the way some view locks as well as our hair in it's natural state. When potential clients come to consult with me about locking their hair there are several points that are crucial to make and discuss before a decision is made to set the date to start the locks. These points also reflect some of the undoing that has to be done from years of hating our true selves and are as follows:

1. *When your hair is natural and healthy there is no such thing as a Hair Emergency!*
2. *Locks are not maintenance free!*
3. *Wearing/starting locks means that you are committed to a change in lifestyle!*
4. *A spiritual transformation will take place: ready or not!*
5. *You will allow your locks to experience a full Life Span!*
6. *You have let go of the plethora of products and will stick with a few that work!*
7. *You have your circle of support in place!*
8. *You have identified books, pictures, etc. for encouragement!*
9. *You know and fully understand the stages of locks!*
10. *You are prepared to cope with all comments you will get and honor your locks!*

During the consultation I always ask clients what their loved ones will think about them locking their hair. I have heard many things that have made me laugh and cry, literally.

Sometimes, it is our families and loved ones that give us the hardest time. I locked my hair to honor my mother, but she had already passed away and to be honest I don't believe that she would have had a problem with it. My sisters were already supportive of my locking, but they were watching to see if this would be something they would try. You know, my being the middle child I never really had a problem being the brave experimental project.

It was my co-workers that I had the most drama and even that was minor. I worked in a paramilitary environment and worked in a very male–dominated office. They even had rules and regulations about hair, especially black hair (meaning braids, locks, twists, and cornrows) that continues to be challenged by some of the workers even today. Because I was a civilian in this environment, the hair rules did not apply to me and some officers higher in rank would push rules and wear natural hairstyles. I took Pamela Farrell's book "Lets Talk Hair" to work with me and explained it to superior officers in charge that might have something to say. I told them I was going to lock my hair and to my surprise they were very supportive! I know that part of their response had to do with them already thinking that me wearing locks would make sense because I wear "ethnic" clothing and had an "ethnic" attitude. One white female officer was totally ignorant to locks and came into my office with her handcuffs and said, "I'll lock your hair up, come with me" and pointed to the holding area for prisoners. We all laughed, but when I twisted my hair for locks I still had to go there to do a job. There was this one officer who worked at the front desk and everybody has to walk by him to get to his or her workstations. Everyday I'd walk past and he would pick up the phone and pretend he was talking to this famous twenty-four hour beauty salon in Detroit called Charlene's and say, "Yeah, Charlene's we got a hair emergency walking in the door, I will put her in the scout car and we'll be right over." Everyday he'd do that, then when it started growing, he'd give me compliments and when I groomed my locks he'd come by my desk and say, "looking good…just checking." This experience made me believe one thing. Brothers don't really care if your hair is nappy, they just like it LONG! I don't know why that is, but most locked sisters can testify to that phenomenon. So if your thinking about locking or have started locking, know that with patience and good grooming you will have the locks you've been dreaming of, and your loved ones will eventually come around, but if they don't, oh well. It's their issue, not yours.

The ten topics of discussion for starting locks listed earlier is the beginning to understanding how wearing locks is an expression that you have evolved from needing hair that is not naturally aesthetic or pleasing to you or your hair. You have accepted that God gave you hair that is nappy and it is okay to work with it. One of my clients, Ella said at one of our PicNap™ events, "…If God wanted you to have straight hair; you would have been born with a straightening comb in your hand…" Amen.

Well Being and Recovery

Starting Locks as an Option for Healing/EcoNap

I hope that thus far we have established that having locks are not only for style, but also for healthy living as well as for women who are searching to find a way to express her inner beauty by accepting how her hair actually is. Emotional healing can be evidenced by your ability to articulate and experience a level of acceptance that biologically your hair is not straight, but curly, full of coils, tight and nappy. Having a positive regard for your nappy hair and feeling good about it within the core of yourself, irregardless to the negative messages you have been given since birth about your natural hair, is key to your emotional well being. To wear your hair in an Afro, twists, cornrows, or extension braids is liberating as well. However, to wear your hair in locks speaks to a whole other level of liberation.

Upon deciding that you will lock your hair it is also understood that you have let go of the American beauty standard and are willing and ready to come out of hiding from your naturally beautiful hair. In doing so, I have adapted a social work tool for assessing individuals that will lock their hair. The Ecomap is a tool used by social workers and will assist the client in taking a better look at their social and family environments and help them identify problem areas to work on so that the life experience is optimal. Because the tool has been adapted we will also rename it. An Ecomap looks at the person in the environment, therefore our tool will be called an Ecomap.

The EcoNap will identify things in her environment that will impact her decision to lock and her relationship with it. In other words, we will look at her community, church, job, peers, family, support systems and resources and determine whether these relationships reflect peace/conflict, balance/imbalance, positivism/negativity, flow/blockage towards locking her hair and work towards identifying and reflecting on those interactions which best support her choice. In addition we will also look at her maternal family of origin and identify hair textures, presence of chemicals in the hair for straightening and other factors, which may shape her attitude towards her hair with the goal of demystifying any myths or misperceptions about her hair. Please review this tool in the illustration provided and determine where you are and whether or not conditions in your environment are or were conducive to locking.

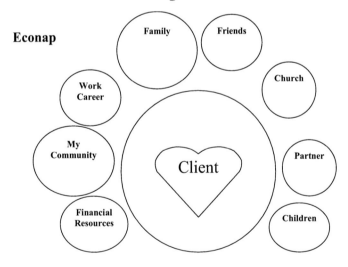

This is how an EcoNap should be drawn by consultant with client during initial hair visit. This is an example; however let the person who wants to lock the option to identify what systems or influences she believes will impact her locking her hair. Here, it is the clients' family, friends, church, partner, children, financial resources, community, and work-life she will have to grapple with as she considers wearing locks as an option for well-being and recovery from beauty standards set by the dominant culture.

EcoNap of a Client after Consultation:

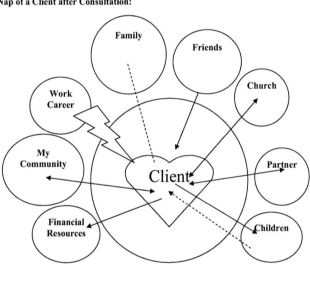

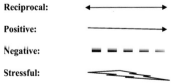

Note: This client explained to the consultant that in terms of locking her hair she knows that her husband would be very supportive because she took the time to explain the entire process to him. She also explained everything to her children; however they were reluctant because they think locks are ugly. She stated that she spends most of her time in the artistic community and thinks this system would respond very well to her locking her hair. Her extended family would have the most problems with her locking because they always have tried to keep all members of the family homogenous with straight hair, which is commonplace for them. She indicated that work life was stressful in general and it's a corporate setting and no one has locks in her environment so she would be the first and expects some backlash as a result. Her friends are supportive and she knows that she can depend on them to encourage her and show her love as she locks her hair. Lastly, she has been saving money and shopping around for prices on natural hair care and is prepared to pay for services.

So, now that the decision has been made to lock your hair it is time to discuss some of the many benefits, besides the growth potential.

Growing Locks as an Option for Well Being

Here is were the locking gets good, what is about to be discussed will either get you started on your way to locks or validate your current or past experience with locks. Now that my locks have a few years on them let me tell you how good they have been to me. Let's start with the weather. Rain or shine, humid or dry, cloudy or muggy, it doesn't matter my locks will still withstand it all and look the same as it did when I left the house for the day. I can go on vacation, get them wet and won't have to go looking for a stylist, hot comb or blow dryer (if in the sun) to make the hair act right. I can crimp, curl and crinkle my locks without adding any heat to my hair at all. I can go work out at the gym the same day I get my hair groomed by the loctician and not waste a dime because it will look the same if I tie it up when I am done. Let's break it on down, locks are one of the healthiest ways to wear your hair because you don't have many ways to damage it, it's long lasting and can hold a style for weeks and can grow to lengths you ain't never seen before. My hair has never been this long, strong and healthy in my life! Locks are not maintenance free but with the help of a loctician from time to time and a simple regiment of washing, conditioning and grooming it is definitely fuss free, I'll tell you that!

In providing lock services I have had many clients share with me the benefits of having locked hair and how it has contributed to their overall well-being. From being able to make love without worrying about a piece of weave being on the pillow when the lights come on; to not having to sleep with your head in your hand or sitting straight up in bed to avoid jacking up that new hairdo you just paid for and can't maintain. One of my clients told me that she bought a silk pillowcase and now does not even wrap her hair up at night and benefits from it because wearing anything on her head gives her a headache. While I encourage folks to wrap the locks up at night with a silk scarf or bonnet, I certainly was not against this sister finding her niche for taking care of her locks the way she saw fit, especially because her locks are healthy.

Growing locks and living through the stages of locks also provide a proven ground for building capacity for patience and tolerance in such a fast paced world. We live in a society where we have to have everything now. We rush things and something gets lost in the process. We sisters sometimes don't want to wait for long locks, we want it now, so we go and get extension locks. Now don't get me wrong, extension locks are cool for style as well as transitioning into natural locks, however there are few if any lessons to learn in doing it the fast route. Even though the Sisterlocks™ system puts your hair in a "locked" position at the first locking session you still have stages to go through that will lend itself to teaching patience (and look good while doing so I might add). Locking the hair naturally teaches us how to love our hair, appreciate time and develop patience, which can help us become better women in general when dealing with everyday tasks that are challenging and daunting at best. I have even witnessed myself, clients who presented at the first consultation as pushy, rushed people become more laid back, conscious individuals after starting the locking process and even report feeling more at ease with the environment, less hostile towards other living things and yes report a higher sense of well-being and have credited that to the process of locking their hair.

Wearing Locks as an Option for Personal Growth and Freedom

We have already established that starting and growing locks lends itself to emotional healing and well-being, now wearing your locks in the world to express your personal growth and freedom is something else to explore. Personal growth reflects evolving into a person whom you can be proud of, satisfied with and willing to share with others for the purpose of fulfilling your greatest potential. Freedom has been defined by the American Heritage Dictionary as, "…not being bound nor obligated to a set of standards and not being affected by a given condition or circumstance in one's experience…" (Paraphrased). Growth and freedom are very forward thinking concepts; however these concepts are available to you and can be manifested in how you manage your life as well as wear your hair.

Another client that started wearing locked hair told me that she never really felt like her outer appearance reflected her inner being. She said she had a "locked mind" and that she was committed to health, well-being, and fair/equal treatment of all living things. She did not eat meat or processed food but her hair was processed and chemically treated for decades. She went on to say that her outward actions did not match her hair either. She was an activist on many different fronts but had not realized that the jerry curl and/or relaxer was an outward denial of herself and the very standards she set forth in her life overall. I must say that now that this sister is locked she has truly become one with herself and now her outward beauty directly reflects her inner beauty and peace. We all have the right to express ourselves in this manner and it is my hope that we get to a point where we can validate what we believe in our hearts about freedom and growth by showing the world that straight hair is not the standard but our hair "as is" is the highest reflection of honor and respect to ourselves.

How to Start Locks

On Your Own

Many women will decide to lock their hair on their own for various reasons. There are many ways to do so and I hope this section will tell you how to do it and get you on your way to beautiful locks.

If you have to grow out of a perm there are several ways to do so. Getting cornrows, natural or extensions are a good option and it may take anywhere from six months to over a year to grow out of a perm. You may also get a weave where the hair is braided to the scalp and wefts of hair are sewn on to the braids and it provides an option to grow out of a perm without exposing the hair to the breakage that can occur due to the hair being handled too much while growing out of the chemical. Wet sets or straw sets are also good options to growing out of a perm; it also gives you a twisted or natural look to help you adjust to wearing your hair in a style that looks close to nappy or kinky. Wigs are always an option to wear and I suggest maybe wearing wigs that look natural, like an Afro or textured wig or braided wigs instead of the straight ones.

Depending on how you want your locks to look will depend on how you start them. First you should wash and condition the hair with products that will not change the texture of your hair. For well-defined locks you and a friend can section your hair into parting sizes that are no smaller than the space between the two defining lines on your baby finger and twist the hair with your fingers or palm roll the hair using a light water-based gel and a light oil such as jojoba. For organic locks that are not as well defined you can wash and condition the hair (preferably start with short hair) and towel-dry the hair in a circular motion and the locks will form on its own. If your natural hair is long you might want to twist sections of your hair then clamp each section down with a hair clip as you go along. Once the entire head is done you should hand dry it on medium to low heat, remove the clips and tie it up at night to help keep them secure.

Once a week you should refresh your locks by using an antiseptic to spray/mist it on your hair. Take a small towel or gauze and wipe between your parts to help clean the locks. Every three to four weeks you should gently wash the locks and re-twist the new growth and palm roll each lock. Make sure that the sections you started are what stay together. Keep up this regiment and you will be on your way. As needed when the locks grow and develop some you can also give yourself hot oil treatments, however I would not recommend this when the locks are new because the newly formed locks are very sensitive to products and the fewer used the better, in my opinion. You may also refer to the methods section of this book to gain insight and get ideas on how to start and maintain your beautiful locks.

Professional Start

To find a professional lock stylist your best bet is to go with someone whose work you are familiar with. It is also a good thing to have had the opportunity to consult with this stylist before setting your first appointment. During the initial consultation certain things should be discussed such as price, time it will take to provide the service, tour of the facility, and any questions you have should be addressed as well as pictures available to determine the method, size and long/short outcomes of locking your hair. As discussed earlier, a determination of your "locability" should be explored via a question and answer session regarding your hair history and belief system regarding wearing your natural hair. To determine if you and the stylist are on the same page and in the same vehicle (be it bus, train, boat or automobile just as long as we get there) the ten understandings mentioned earlier in this book, should also be reviewed and discussed.

As a lock stylist I tend to be eclectic in my approach towards locking hair. When a customer tells me what she wants, I look at her hair and determine which route will be best for her, present the idea and see if we are in agreement. I also believe that there is more than one way to get to beautiful locks and to learn more about this lets approach the topic method by method.

Methods

One Strand Comb Twists

The lock stylist will start in the back of the head and apply one part about a half inch above the nap of the neck from right to left, then proceed to make parted sections on wet and washed hair about the size no smaller or bigger than the section of space between the two lines in the middle of your baby finger. Each section is then twisted with a water-based gel with the smallest end of a barbers comb. The hand motions are similar to the way a hand would motion if using curling irons that roll and put on a stove. This motion occurs until all the hair has been successfully winded into itself forming a coil. Once all the coils have been placed into the hair a light oil is applied by misting the hair with it, then the person is placed under a dryer under medium to low heat until dry. When the client returns for grooming, wash the hair, separate the locks, apply oil and retwist/palmroll each lock and use a clip to hold in place until dry. A comb may be used to re-twist the new growth, depending on the skill of the lock stylist, being careful not to comb through the portion of the hair that is starting to lock. Light oil can also be applied before twisting/coiling the hair as well. Some customers prefer to air dry and if the temperature outside is above 75 degrees I may let them get away with it. However, it is very important to let the hair dry because you don't want to get mildew in your locks and that can easily happen when wearing wet or waterlogged locks.

Two Strand Hand Twists

Keep the parting system the same as with one strand twists; however instead of comb twisting you will use both hands to intertwine the hair and combine them by folding one section of hair over the other until you reach the ends. Upon a returned visit for grooming, wash the hair, locate the already parted sections, keep the two stranded twists together and re-twist the new-growth and palm roll the body of the twists, clip to hold in place and allow hair to dry. This method is primarily used for individuals who want to start their locks with hair that is six inches or longer or for textures which may not agree with the one strand method or for those who like the two stranded look better than the one strand comb twists. Although I highly recommend the one strand option, the two-strand method will yield good results as well.

Palm Rolls

This method may result in locks that appear less cultivated and the parting system may not be as defined. However, this is a wonderful option to those who do not wish to use a comb in starting their locks. A section of hair is selected while wet and placed into the palm of both hands, and then the hands move in one direction until a coil is created. Light oil, aloe (from the plant or manufactured) and/or a water-based gel will help set the locks in place, but not required. Clips are optional and helpful.

Organic

Just wash the hair and watch it. Don't comb it. Dry it in a circular motion with a towel. Oil lightly once, twice or three times a week. See what happens in a few months to a year. Beautiful!

Sisterlocks™

As a Sisterlocks Consultant for the past four years I can say that this is a very intense, involved and well-developed system for starting and maintaining smaller locks. Created by Dr. JoAnne Cornwell the Sisterlocks technique is one that has to be taught by a trained and certified Sisterlocks teacher/instructor. An advantage to having Sisterlocks is that a person can still keep a perm, thereby keeping length (with 1 to 2 inches of new growth) and still start locking. Trademark and other legalities in place prevent me from sharing too much about this system, however if you wish to learn more you may go to www.sisterlocks.com. I will also say that if you want Sisterlocks be prepared to spend significantly more time and money for them and the results they yield are just as beautiful as traditional locks and the choice is yours to make. I just love options, don't you?

Now, I do have a wonderful Sisterlocks story to share and I figure this would be as good a time as any to share it. When I first heard of Sisterlocks, I had gotten the wrong impression. I thought that Sisterlocks were being promoted as the "better" locks and based on what I have said in this book you know I wasn't feeling that. So, I opted not to provide it as a service. Until one day, a sister contacted me by the name of Stefanie Fields-Bradley who wanted Sisterlocks (*see her picture). She worked as a sales manager for a local radio station. I honored her, explained to her that I did not provide the service and I referred her to Everette's Cornrows and Braiding Academy where they not only provide the service but also taught the class on Sisterlocks.

That's what good social workers do; send you to the right place if they can't help you. Well Stefanie called me back and stated that she was uncomfortable going there because she did not know anyone over there. Now, that tickled me because she did not know me either and when I expressed that, she went on to say that a person whom she trusted (Gwen Winston) had referred her to me and would like for me to do her Sisterlocks and I still declined. However, I offered to set up an appointment and go with her to the Sisterlocks consultation at Everette's with Sheila Everette-Hale. She picked me up from my home and we went together and let me testify and tell you how spirit worked in my life. Sheila asked why do I keep blocking my blessings by sending her all these referrals for Sisterlocks when she knows I can do them myself and earn a living as well as add to the services I was providing and my answer was null and based on lack of knowledge. I heard myself saying nothing so I said, "Well what do you want me to do about it"? She said, "Take the class and do your friends' hair."

We laughed because up until that afternoon we were strangers, so I asked the next obvious question, "How much is the class, Sheila?" After telling me how much, I immediately said that I could not afford it, "…so go on ahead and give this woman her consultation and set a date for her locking session with one of the stylists here" is what I said. Well Stefanie said, "I'll pay for the class and you repay me by doing my hair." I said, "You are joking, right?" She said, "No, I am not and Sheila, can't you use some air time promoting your school and salon?" and Sheila started praising the Lord (she's genuinely good at giving God all the glory-all the time which is why I love her so much) then they went in the back and the next thing I know I registered for the class. Because of this experience I will always honor Dr. Cornwell and her creativity towards providing us with one more option in locking our hair and thanks to Sheila and Stefanie for seeing something in me I didn't even know I had, which was the ability to expand my knowledge base and capacity for cultivating Sisterlocks™.

Here is Stefanie in her crown of beautiful Sisterlocks:

Interlocks/Stitchlocks/Latchlocks

Depending on where you are from will depend on what you call this method. This method is done for the purpose of making smaller locks. Akin to Sisterlocks™ a latch hook tool is used when touching up the locks. These locks can start with comb twists or coils and/or a reversed braid can be placed into the virgin/natural hair to begin. There is no specific parting system but it tends to be similar to the parting used for comb twists, however the parts can be smaller (at least half the size). The hair should be washed and this technique can be applied when the hair is wet or dry. Wet hair gives better and won't cause as much breakage while putting the locks in. Initially this lock might resemble a braid. This is the method I use for my locks and it is because I like the tightness of the new growth after being done. Here's why: While getting my hair braided I became addicted to the tight feeling at the scalp and still need that feeling to experience that fresh idea that I just got my hair done. Did I mention that we are all works in progress? I admit it.

Stages of Locks & The Well Being Connection

I will not only describe the stages of locks like many master locticians have described in the past, but I will also describe behaviors that have been prominently expressed by some clients that go along with each stage. Also, instead of covering every possibility, what I will do is explain "typical" experiences by clients who may come to see me. However, please know that there is not a "typical" situation nor "perfect" but I will describe desired outcomes and common manifestations. The reason for this approach is to help prepare the person who is considering locking their hair as well as put language to behaviors that may baffle service providers and confuse customers alike. Understanding and thinking about the stages in this framework will limit if not eliminate frustration that comes from starting locks and hopefully will alleviate anxious feelings when on this journey towards locks. Locks occur and grow similar to our life span; therefore I have broken down the stages in the same way and adapted these stages from masters Nekhena Evans, Tulani Kinard, and Pamela Ferrell. Also, I'd like to credit my clients for teaching me about the stages and I honor them for being available to this purpose and allowing me to share their stories.

0-6 Months-The Infancy Stage

Baby Locs

This is when the locks are brand new and placed into to hair to begin the process. Some may refer to this stage as the "baby" stage. Comb coils are placed into the hair, which appear as shiny, cute, bouncy, little spirally curls. Almost everyone will want to know about your hair as well as request to touch it. Just like how folks act when newborn babies arrive. They want to hold her and kiss her and touch her and know her name and tickle her, etc. Your job as the new lock wearer is to be mindful of who you allow the chance to touch and learn your hair. Treat it as you would your baby. Actually, you practically will treat them like babies, you will tend to watch them for long periods of time, constantly check on them, are very gentle with them and you might even be overly protective of them as well. You will call your loctician at anytime, day or night to confirm that the babies are doing what they should and you may even keep a journal. In fact, I encourage you to keep a diary or log if it makes you feel better during this initial phase.

Your visit back to the loctician (3-4 weeks) will consist of a wash so gentle that it might make you mad. Others are just glad to have some water on the babies at all. In between visits you might want to use an astringent such as Seabreeze™ or diluted lemon water to freshen your baby locks and use oil to lubricate and moisturize them no more than three times a week. Keep it tied up at night with a silk scarf or bonnet. Your lock stylist will groom your locks and they will not look like they did the last time you were in the chair. The locks will probably be longer and they may or may not lay down, so get ready, because you ain't seen nothing yet!

6-12 Months-The Puberty Stage

Teen Locs

Actually, the times that I have identified for all lock stages are not a hard science. Rather they are estimates that are very generous so that you will be prepared for the long and short of the process. With that being said, the puberty stage may happen as early as a month after your initial twists were placed into your hair for locks. I am very visual when it comes to locks and the way I describe this stage and it's process is by using my hands. Picture the palm of your hand as your head and your fingers are your twists/locks, the line that is at the bottom of each finger, which is connected to your palm, is your scalp. The lines that are in the middle of your fingers (which represent the new locks) will expand, the end of the twist will still be in place; however the end that is closest to the scalp will grow and become loose and should be re-twisted during grooming sessions. This look is the first indication that you are growing into your puberty stage of the locking process. It looks as though the lock is pregnant. Most lock stylists refer to this as the bulb; eventually this bulb will tighten and shrink back down to the same size as the rest of the lock. Once that happens, the lock will continue to matt together from that point to the ends. When that is complete, the lock will then matt from the other end of the initial bulb to the scalp and continue to lock in that direction throughout the duration of the life span.

*Note: I cannot stress enough that although I have given time frames for this process, I have witnessed with my own eyes a sister who got her twists for the first time come out of the dryer with bulbs well defined in her locks within minutes! It was amazing to see.

During this stage, the locks are trying to find their own way. They will sit however they want and need room to grow and just be. I don't care how much you tie them up or twist them or tie them down or how many appointments you "try" to get in to see your lock stylist…they won't do anything you might want them to do. So, get some head wraps or let it go and let it be and keep your scheduled appointments with your stylist and/or continue with your grooming schedule. There is a thing as twisting too much so I suggest that you just wait it out until the locks gain some length and weight and trust me they will fall how you want them, just not now.

Behaviors on the part of the person locking that may manifest during this period include but are not limited to the serious consideration of starting over, taking them down altogether, resulting to wearing wigs, hats, scarves and placing undo pressure on the lock stylist to make the locks "do" something else other than look like this. I have also heard clients call this the "ugly" or "awkward" stage, which I try to discourage them from saying because it is so negative. Speaking words into the universe are so powerful, so why not say good things about your locks? Frame of mind is everything when considering your attitude towards a particular situation. Imagine this as the teenager in your home or a young person you have mentored, would you call them ugly or give up on them or tear them down? I think not. As a matter of fact, I have spoken with sisters who actually miss this stage once they are beyond it and they celebrate customers who are in this stage and try to offer support to them right in the shop as they see newer lock wearers at this point in the process. Gracefully accept the support if needed and try your best not to let the look keep you from your goal of having locks. And this too shall pass.

12-18 Months-The Adult Stage

Adult Locs

This is when the locks tend to perform very well. The lock stylist and/or the client can begin to explore many styling options and the locks have some length to them. The formation of the locks are solid and the lock wearer may notice that grooming may not take as long (unless other factors are in place beyond grooming). The locks respond very well to the palm rolling technique and are stronger. The washing of the locks can be more vigorous and can tolerate a good scalp message while wet without the fear of them coming down. The locks are adults and are pretty much locking on their own, a pattern or grid, or DNA respectively has been formed and the locked hair is now replicating itself. During this time, lock stylists might consider pruning the locks for excess hair that does not matt along the shaft of the locks. Also, this may be a time where some locks may not be strong enough to survive on their own (for any given reason) and may need to be joined together with another lock (also known as families).

So now that the hair is grown-up, the lock wearer/client begins to feel more confident in the care and wear of the locks. So much that they may not visit the lock stylist as much and they may even try styles and grooming on their own. The stylist should encourage independence with clients on some level (keeping in mind that we lock stylists still do need to earn a living). Therefore, individuals who wear locks should be supported by their lock stylists in order to be comfortable with their own hair. If the service is great, they will come back, this is just part of the growing process. This is liberation work right? This is where it would benefit the lock stylist to provide styling options/treatments that every lock wearer could take advantage of to keep them coming.

18-36 Months + Elder Stage

Elder Locs

This is the time that the locks become rooted. The growth potential has far exceeded your expectations and you will hear comments from other folks concerning how long might you keep your locks and wondering when will you cut them out. Maintenance is pretty much the same and grooming consists of similar techniques used during the adult stage. However, now you may volunteer to wash your locks before visiting with the lock stylist because it is easier for you to wash them while in the shower. In addition, your locks are so long they probably can't fit in any average sink anymore for washing. If you started your locks before you had gray hair, you may have a little now. Oxidation may also have occurred, which is the natural lightening of the hair due to the sun and other factors. You and your locks are one; it's an integral part of your identity.

People may even describe you by your mature locks. What may occur in elder locks is about one to two inches of the lock may just slide off the bottom tip to naturally relieve itself of weight. This is natural and should happen; do not attempt to reattach it because it still needs to be relieved of the weight. Moisturizing the locks is important at all phases, but especially this stage. Some clients say that they will keep their locks for a lifetime, others start talking about cutting them out once in the elder stage (if not before) and based on what I stated, in the ten understandings, listed in Chapter 2, this is actually a time that may be appropriate to consider it. In other words, because of the life span stages of locks it does not shock me (anymore) that cutting the locks out have been at least thought about at this stage. Oh, but this stage is regal! All I can say is enjoy your rooted locks to the fullest and honor this stage and watch others honor you. New lock wearers will approach you and look to you for information and support. Just like we look to and honor our elders in the community for love and guidance.

In Social Work practice we learn group dynamic techniques when watching people grow and develop and work together towards a goal. The order in which this happens over time is the exact way that locks form. It is the action of Forming, Storming, Norming and Performing. Forming would be considered when the locks are first created and look and act like babies on the hair. Storming is the puberty stage when struggling to lock your hair is at it's greatest. Norming is when the locks are just a part of who you are and you are very comfortable with them. And lastly, performing is when the locks are showing their fullest lock growth potential and you have evolved into appreciating your locks and loving them-as is.

Healing for your Hair and Overall Well-Being

Note:

I suggest that you speak with a medical doctor before changing eating or exercise habits. Pregnant and nursing women should also consult with a physician when considering the use of herbal products. This section of the book is not intended to replace advice that one should obtain from a medical professional.

How to Take Care of your Locks

Locks are by no means maintenance free; however they are relatively simple to take care of. After you have had your twists/baby locks placed into the hair as a lock wearer you should tie your hair up every night with a silk scarf or bonnet. In the early stages washing can be tricky, however if you are gentle and if you re-twist it from the original base you should do fine. Palm rolling the entire lock once it is long enough to fit in the base of your hands, works best (see how to chapter). Most lock wearers who have the majority of their maintenance done by a natural hair care provider can use Seabreeze and gauze to cleanse the base once a week to freshen and remove oil or product build up and/or bacteria from the hair and scalp between visits. Light oil can be used sparingly several times a week to promote a healthy glow and prevent dryness. Hot oil treatments once or every other month also helps keep the locks supple.

What to Eat for your Locks

Whole grains, in-season fruits and vegetables should be abundant in your diet, whether you have locks or not. 8-10 eight ounce glasses of water also help with the tone of your skin and scalp. Avoid high fat, red meat, pork and high sodium intake in your diet. Some of the foods you eat can also help your locks on the outside as well. Olive oil is a great substance for inside and out. You can use olive oil on your salads, while cooking/ baking and on your hair for a hot oil treatment. Nuts are also a good source of protein and can be eaten sparingly because of the high fat content. Exercise will also help with improved circulation, which will promote hair growth.

What to Smell for your Locks

Sage

Not just good for your mama's Thanksgiving dressing but serves as an energy cleanser and aromatically therapeutic if burned like incense. In the hair it works best on darker hues and serves as an antiseptic.

Tea Tree

Found in brands such as Melaleuca™, Aveda, and IC, tea tree smells great and serves as a fungus and bacteria killer. Natural tea tree oil works best diluted in water or in an oil carrier.

Jojoba

This particular oil is special in that it resembles *sebum,* which is the oil that is naturally produced by the scalp. It is light and has a fresh smell. Jojoba also washes from the hair the best and works great as an all over body moisturizer.

Lavender

Use dried lavender leaves in a glass container as a room/air freshener. Lavender oil works well in the hair with a carrier and can provide soothing to scalp/skin irritations and relieves an itchy scalp.

Rosemary

Not just for your best, baked chicken dish, rosemary can aid the hair by providing defense against flaking and dandruff; it can also stimulate the scalp and follicles. Rosemary also has the ability to help locks glisten and glow.

Nettle

Although many hair company's use nettle in their products they don't hardly use it enough! Nettle when purchased in its raw form can be brewed down into a tea rinse and used as a leave in before grooming and/or styling.

Peppermint

Can be used in many hair recipes to stimulate the scalp and wake up the hair follicles. It should be used in conjunction with other oils to give it a sweeter smell. It also can be used as a cleanser and rinse after shampooing the locks.

Lemon

A natural cleanser, lemon juice/oil can be diluted with water and used to re-freshen the hair between washes.

Considering Commercial Products for Locks

Right off the top I will tell you what product lines I trust when it comes to locks. Aveda, Melaleuca™, Sisterlocks™ and Black Earth. Luckily enough for us that locks are becoming so popular that we have a plethora of products to choose from. There are many small black owned companies making products for locks and it would be best if you, the reader, refer to the World Wide Web to find them. While looking on the Internet, here are some things you should know about locks and commercial products:

1.

Creams, bees wax, mineral oil, shea based products cause the most build up damage over time.

2.

Petroleum products should never be used on locks.

3.

If there are products on the market that you like and they have any of the aforementioned, please be certain that it is not the main base of the product as evidenced by these products being listed first in the ingredients.

4.

If you use these products anyway, please do so informed and sparingly.

5.

Thando Kefele of Brooklyn New York says, "Oil, gel and water" for lock maintenance and healthy glowing/growing locks and I believed him. My experience has yielded this to be very true.

6.

All gels used for lock grooming should be water or aloe based. Nekhena Evans of New Bein' says, "Why not just go to the health food store and purchase the aloe plant, cut it open and scrape the gel...then use it for styling and grooming the locks" I respect and honor her. My experience has proven her correct, this is time consuming, so I settle for the less potent store bought version and it works almost as well.

Coloring your Locks

Out of respect for cosmetology rules in the United States, I don't perform any hair procedures that require a license. So I won't color locks, unless the customer signs a waiver. I color my locks every six months to one year, very successfully, but I like being on the safe side of state regulation whether I agree with it or not. Here is where I use my skills in social work and refer the client to a competent, licensed colorist to provide that service.

If coloring is done right by a colorist, then there should be no problems. As a matter of fact, color can add some life and jazz to a set of locks. Coloring is also used to camouflage embedded lint in locks and can serve as a wonderful change if desired. Coloring your locks will cause dryness and may make them brittle, so make sure you moisturize on a regular basis…then watch out for product build up.

Remedy for Product Build-Up

Soak the locks in the hottest water tolerable, wash with a shampoo that has product break down capacity, ring the hair and rinse twice with hot water. Re-twist the hair without products in sections of 4-8 locks. Braid the locks by squeezing the excess water and product from the hair. Take an absorbent towel and squeeze the braided locks until the excess product is visible in the towel. Repeat this regiment every 3-4 weeks until better results yield. Also you can mix baking soda with water to create a paste and place it on the locks, let sit for 10 minutes, rinse with apple vinegar cider and wash with your usual shampoo using very warm water until clear.

Kalimah Johnson

Poetry and Pictures

As Is…

I started with in mind that I would cultivate natural black hair
Introduce to mankind the organic verse
Remove the curse if I dare
Some call it dreads
But that terminology is dead
I don't know how one could ever regret
The coil of the black head
Wire like and full of wooly textures
Sensual and sexual
The topic of many lectures and
If your nappy and you know it…clap your hands
See, locks are more than what you see among the raga
muffin bands
From the sands of Khemet
From the urban curbs and alleyways…
The vibe of the lock I send it
To show praise to the beautiful and brave
So to the ones that twist and shout I know it's not a joke
And to my friends who wax them ends and woven like
tight jump rope
I respect and honor you
I am locked because of you
I love my hair just like you do
And I thank you for being true
As you are and as is…

Women who have made the Well Being Connection

I present to you sisters who have made the well being connection and locked their hair! They are women who come from all walks of life and wanted to share their stories with you. I have selected several women here for brevity, but know that there are many other women in the world who are very excited about their newfound freedom in wearing locks! What you the reader will see here is the women responses with very few edits, as I did not want to impose my thinking on them. Some sisters decided to answer the questions verbatim and others restructured the questions altogether…what I hope you get out of their stories is hope, encouragement and incite.

In asking them to participate in this book, I asked several questions which are listed here:

*When and why did you decide to lock your hair?

*Did a professional start your locks and/or did you start them yourself or have a friend help you?

*What benefits have you gained from locking your hair? Physical, Mental, Spiritual, Emotional?

*What was the worst and best thing anyone ever said to you about your locks and who said it?

*What would you say to a black woman (or any woman) who is thinking about locking her hair but has reservations about it?

*Have you learned any lessons from locking your hair, if so, what?

This is what each of them had to say with a picture of their beautiful crown of locs.

Janice-Traditional Locks

Mother/Doctor/Wife

My decision to lock my hair came approximately 10 years ago, after years of dissatisfaction with relaxers, rollers, curling irons, creams, gels, biweekly hair appointments at $50 plus, etc. I knew that natural was the way to go, but had become afraid of my own hair! I started out by cutting my relaxed hair short, then trimmed the relaxer off week by week, and set it on perm rods to get the curly natural look. Finally I had my hair cut into a short afro, which I had groomed every one to two weeks, and wore for two and a half years, while I contemplated and researched; asking others with locks how they did it. I found books, asked my hairstylist, who had no experience with natural hair. In fact I knew of only two stylists in Detroit! Braiders even seemed hard to find. Six years ago I decided to just go for it and use all the knowledge I had acquired and start my own locks.

I hesitated having a professional start my locks. There were few locticians in the city when I started, and I had heard of them through their clients I had approached and asked about their hair. As I recall, most seemed lukewarm about their stylist and had suggestions about locking themselves. So, one night, a friend and I started two strand twists on my newly grown out natural curly afro. The original locks washed out during a trip to Mexico a month later (I had to wash after being in the ocean, you know), so my girlfriend and I had to restart them, and I think we did better the second time around in terms of parting. Six months later, a colleague of mine who locked spoke so enthusiastically about her loctician, I had to give her a try, and five years later I'm hooked on someone else doing my hair and loving it!

At first, I was self conscious with my locks in the beginning because of the negative connotation locks have for some people. Not to mention that my hair had a life of its own! I receive more compliments on my hair, which has definitely boosted my ego (so did wearing my hair in a short natural). I am proud to be a successful Black woman and my locks are my crown. I feel regal wearing them. I can say it has been the best decision I ever made to enhance my appearance.

When Kalimah asked me what was the worst and best thing anyone ever said to me about my locks and who was it that said it, it made me think of this white woman who once exclaimed to me after seeing (and feeling) my locks, "Oh they are soft, that's not what I would expect". Many people (Black and White) think my hair is braided, but most give wonderful compliments about how beautiful they are!

I tell anyone thinking of locking-Go for it! It is a personal, intense decision though, 'cause you know how we are about our hair. If you have been using chemicals, ditch them. Become comfortable with your natural texture. I remind them that's it's not permanent until your hair locks, so what do you have to lose? Then I refer them to my loctician!

I have learned to have Patience, Patience, Patience!

Katrina-Interlocks

Mother/Police Officer/Wife

I locked my hair about three years ago, because I was tired of the chemical process.

A friend started my locks but a professional lock stylist now maintains them.

The benefits I've obtained is total freedom of not wasting my valuable time and money in salons only to be disappointed days later by a hairstyle that does not last or can endure a workout.

The best thing someone said to me was that I had a pretty face and that my locks were very becoming on me. The worst thing someone said to me was "you can't wash your hair can you?" I simply replied, "Do you think

I would not wash my hair? If anything I can wash my hair once a week and it will still look the same…what about you?"

I would tell another black woman who is thinking about locking her hair to look at all the time you will have to spend on yourself and your family.

Try to give your hair a break from the chemical process and see how fast your hair will grow without perms and weaves, try something that is natural and much better for your hair and don't buy into the images in the magazines and videos that black women are to be straight haired Barbie dolls.

I've learned that all the while I didn't need perms and weaves to grow my hair…because I was not born with them…all I needed was a way to do something for myself that would make me feel a sense of well being and freedom. My locks set me apart from the norm.

Dee-Sisterlocks

Mother/Poet/Wife/Marathon Runner

I had been mulling over locs for years but didn't think that I could find a style of loc that fit into my lifestyle and that my husband would like. I did some research and in the summer of 2005 decided that Sisterlocks™ were the route for me. I've always felt slightly enslaved to my hair when I wore it in relaxed styles and I hated that feeling. I wanted to be free…free from hair drama, free from touch-ups, free to exercise when and if I wanted, free to love my hair again. Sisterlocks allowed me to know what hair freedom actually meant.

My locs were started by none other than LocMama, Kalimah Johnson and the physical benefit to locking my hair was little to no hair drama. I am actively engaged in active exercise sessions. And thank God… no lesions from perms!

Mentally, I find myself…being myself. I am not worried about whether my hair is defining me. It's not the "last" accessory anymore. I don't worry about this "hair thing" defining me as a living being.

Emotionally, I feel good when I look in the mirror and see the natural state of my hair. It's how it should be. I sense a progression of sorts. It's as if I am growing in esteem because I care more about how I perceive myself rather than how others perceive me.

Spiritually, I believe in the fruits of the Spirit as described in Galatians. It's amazing how God can take the simple things like hair to confound the wise or in my case to teach a lesson. I am notoriously impatient and with the Sisterlocks, I have had to learn the gift of patience--no my hair is not the length I want right now; no, it's not behaving as I had envisioned but my locs are still young and time and patience will prove valuable as they grow and lengthen and "behave" the way I have envisioned them.

Folks always will find reasons to talk about what you are doing with your hair, positive or negative.

However, I really didn't care about the negative things. I do hate it when people call them "dreads" rather than locs but those souls are mostly ill-informed or absent of decorum. The best thing that anyone could have said was when my husband told me he liked them and they looked exactly the way he preferred.

I would say to any woman who is thinking about locking to just wait until you feel it intuitively. I instinctively knew when it was time for me to grow locs. I felt it. Most women, if at all responsive to their own needs, will know when the time is right and strike while the fire is hot. Still, answer one question before you make the choice: Do I know who I am and do I matter to me?

I have learned many lessons, two of them being patience and trust. I know they will be what I want them to be. I just need to trust the process and wait. Black Rapunzels exist but time and patience are her hairdressers!

Kim-Traditional Locks

Talent Manager/Activist

For me, locking my hair was a natural progression from going natural. I'd worn permed hair since I was 12 and decided that I wanted to grow my hair instead of always cutting it for style. This took me to a stylist that only does natural hair and grows you safely out of your perm. After 3 years of wearing the same hairstyle I decided to give locs a try.

I actually started my locs twice; I wanted to have them at a certain length trying to avoid the baby and teen stages. The first time that I loced it was horrific. It was not the look that I wanted for my locs and I had questions on grooming. Because my hair was long I was given a two-strand twist, which was cute for about a week, but I could not see it turning into locs that I would love so I took them out and waited for another year before trying again. My next set of locs were comb twists and though they looked like nothing that I'd seen before I could envision them becoming what I'd dream of having and they have not failed me yet. My love for my hair in its early stages allowed me to be very patient and experimental thus making me more aware of styles yet to come.

I locked my hair for spiritual reasons as well as my being closer to nature through my inner being that I decided to loc. It has been a healthy and welcomed change for me.

Nothing bad or negative has actually been said to my face about my hair. I get teased a lot about needing my hair done, but by that time it DOES really need to be done and that is said out of love. Friends have told me that we are so happy you are in the stage that you are in with your hair now because we didn't know what those things were you had in your hair in the beginning. I think the one thing that does offend me is when folks are shocked that I have actually grown my hair this long thinking that all people with long hair have some sort of extension or hair weave.

I would say to a black woman (or any woman) who is thinking about locking her hair that if you are feeling hesitant then it is not the time for you to loc your hair. Once you are comfortable with the life change of which you are embarking only then should you make the transformation to locs. It is a wonderful change but you can only truly enjoy it when you are truly ready.

I don't feel as though I have learned any lessons from locking my hair, however I may have but don't have the words to articulate it at this time...I'm just glad I did it!

Kendra-Traditional Locks

Real Estate Assessor/African Dancer

I wore my hair in a short natural for eight years prior to changing styles. I decided...

To lock based on the desire to change my natural hairstyle.

I saw a sister in the building where I work, and she had coiled twists.

I really liked them and asked her who did them. She gave me Kalimah Johnson's card. I then wore coiled twists for about a year before I made the decision to lock my hair. I took the decision very seriously, because I viewed it as a long-term commitment.

My locks were started by a master loctician. Kalimah twisted my hair for one year before I decided to lock. She still maintains my locks. I chose Election Day 2001 as the day to start my locks. To me it represented the freedom of choice.

The benefits that I have experienced due to my hair being locked are freedom, cultural expression, and fun. It is actually very fun having locks. I didn't realize how versatile locks could be in terms of styling. My hair has responded so well to being locked; it has never been this healthy and long before.

I haven't had a perm in fifteen years, and my locks allowed me to continue the freedom of being able to get my hair wet in the shower or out in the rain. I don't worry about sweating my hair out when I exercise, and these are just added bonuses. Cultural pride and expression are the major bonuses. I was able to reclaim some of my ancestry, because locks are indigenous to the African Diaspora.

I receive so many compliments on my locks. Complete strangers come up to me and ask how long I've had my locks and tell me that they are beautiful. It makes me feel good when people say that my hair makes them want to lock their hair. Those are the best things, and

I have not yet experienced any negativity about my locks. The closest to negative was when a coworker commented that locks look nice on me, however she didn't have the face or the courage to lock her hair. I actually considered that comment as a lack of consciousness as opposed to negativity.

I would tell any black woman to lock her hair only if she felt totally comfortable with the decision. Although everyone's hair is different I would tell her what to expect with each stage of the locks' growth. I would tell her to ask herself why she wanted locks. If it were just for convenience, then I would recommend that perhaps she rethink the decision to lock her hair. Finally, I would tell her that before she locks to be totally comfortable with her natural hair without chemicals. Whether her natural hair is nappy, kinky, slightly curly, or silky, she should consider it "good hair", because it is hers.

I have learned patience and acceptance as a result of having locks. When I was anxious to get past a certain stage of my locking process, I had no other choice but to wait for my hair to do what it wanted. Accepting this fact allowed me to appreciate the art of patience.

Keelie, Mom and Family-Long Traditional Locks

Social Worker/Promoter/Activist

I decided to lock my hair on 7/1/2000. I truly wanted to lock my hair in 1988 after attending a KRS-One concert at the University of Detroit. My best friend and I attended and I was not supposed to be there. In 1990, after completing high school, my mother told me two things when I left for school, "you can not come home with your nose pierced or growing dred locks". I did neither, so I could return home with peace but if I had it my way, I would have done both. After completing school and returning home, I grew my perm out and had braids from time to time, not knowing what to do but deep down inside, I knew what I should be doing. In 1998, I cut all my hair off and rocked a short afro with plans to start locking. After 2 years, it hit me – What am I waiting for?

In 1990 (at college) I knew I would be different from most, after returning home and having job, I went for my dream to grow locks. I was so concerned about how others would perceive me but I learned along time ago, I must be myself! I wanted to connect with my roots, all natural, no perm, no chemicals, no pressing. I JUST WANTED TO BE FREE!!!!! This helps me to identify with my culture; my skin makes me commit to my people. I love them both.

Kalimah Johnson, who is also my friend, started my locks professionally.

Here are the benefits I have gained since locking my hair:

Emotional: I know I live to a beat that comes from a different drum. I have battled in the past at times to fit in with the norm of friends, co-workers and family. I have to just be myself and my locks allow me to silently express myself.

Physical: I have come to learn that my locks have changed my physical appearance by adding additional beauty and they bring a different type of confidence.

Spiritual: All people are from one origin. My people are the original people. God created me. My locks are inspired by God. Man created the comb. If I ever cut my locks, I must say that my locks have given me additional insight on a spiritual level.

Best thing ever said about my locks…

Busta Rhymes told me "your locks are beautiful (he touched them); don't ever cut them, never!" Just a little insight, let me tell it, Busta is my husband. Now what has happened to his locks? He is still my husband.

Best thing that ever happened…

When I started my locks, my mother never really said anything about them. NOW SHE IS GROWING LOCKS, I love them.

Worst thing ever said…

Nothing bad ever said to my face. People just have questions.

My advice to another black woman…

Stop waiting and giving 101 excuses. Now in our society, locks are accepted when compared to the past. Don't have all the thoughts that they must grow a certain way. Women are too caught up on "hair status". Just be yourself and be free.

Lessons learned…

Patience was not a problem but having courage in this crazy, mixed up society that states western civilization is normal forced me to continue to learn to be me. This challenged me to express the feeling inside of me that was sparked in 1988.

Locks seem to demand a different form of respect on a daily basis from others. It seems that I hear the "Hey Sista" or "Queen" as the fitting nickname when I normally would get no words at all.

Brenda-Traditional Locks

Mom/Activist/Master Gardener

I decided to lock my hair because I was tired of perms and braids and spending so much time and money on my hair. I wanted to be natural and free. Perms and braids felt like I was enslaved to beauty salons and their time.

My locks were started by a professional.

The benefit of locking my hair has been a transforming emotional experience. Having natural hair has taught me to love myself even more. I don't have to conform to what "people think" of me, only what I think of myself and how I want to see me. It's been a wonderful journey!

The best thing anyone ever said to me was "your hair is beautiful/gorgeous, who does your hair" which was said to me when I first started and until this very day. Family, friends and complete strangers say this to me, almost every time I'm out. I have a friend at work who I lunch with everyday and she says she gets tired of people stopping us all the time cutting into our lunch hour asking about my hair. She says whenever you're with me; it's almost guaranteed you will be stopped.

I would tell any woman to take some more time and think about it. I think you have to have a certain amount of maturity to lock your hair. Unless you just want to lock for a style and then cut your hair (I don't recommend that). But if you're really serious, think about it and then go for it! It's a wonderful feeling and experience.

The lesson I've learned is to be You, no matter what people think of what you're doing. You don't have to conform and look like everybody else or hide yourself. In every room I've entered I've stood out because of my hair and everyone was looking at me, and as I enter the room with a big smile on my face, I'm thinking yes, I've arrived!

Kendra-Combination Interlocks and Traditional

Employment Specialist/Mom/Spiritual Teacher

I knew in my early twenties that I would lock my hair. My plan was to begin my process on my 40th birthday. However, as time changed I decided to begin my process a few years ahead of schedule. By the time I turn 40 my locks will be 4 years old.

My friend is a master loctician and she began my process.

There is a sense of freedom that I have gained from allowing my hair to lock. As I stated earlier, I knew in my twenties that I would lock my hair. I was committed to relaxing my hair and keeping with the lastest hair trends in my youth. However, within me I knew that as I matured I would no longer be a slave to chemicals or societies standards of beauty. Physically, I have accepted my hair and its natural beauty. Mentally, I no longer stress over being in a shop for 3-5 hours every two weeks. Nor do I have to torture myself with the strong relaxers. Spiritually, I am growing more in GOD with just accepting all of me as a beautiful expression of God. I am happy, whole and complete as a free black woman in America. Therefore, emotionally I am free to be me. Freedom is a great place and space to rest in. Thank You God for freedom.

The worst thing someone said to me during my process was "Why you are locking, because you don't want to comb your hair anymore?" The best is when people (especially other sisters) who have locks (or desire to lock) compliment me on how beautiful I am and how much they love my hair.

I would say to any black woman who is thinking about locking to pray about it and ask the question, "What do I have to lose if this is what I truly desire?" I would ask, "If you truly desire to lock are you going to embrace your new journey?" If you are concerned with what others think about you or will it be received within your work environment again the question is "will this make me happy". If you are strong, confident and secure, you will move forward. If you are still trying to figure out who you are then wait. The answer will always present itself in due time and season. Trust the process.

I have learned that freedom is priceless. As long as I am a black woman living in America I have made a conscience decision to embrace all of me and that is good. Whether, I have long flowing locks or a short crop of locks, it matters about how pleased I am with me. Society does not inform me of my beauty. I have transformed into all that God has created me to be and I am all-good. Freedom is priceless and I am truly free!

Dondrea-Traditional Locks

Wife/MBA/Artist

WHEN & WHY DID YOU DECIDE TO LOCK YOUR HAIR?

After about four years of contemplating if I should lock, I decided to go ahead and take the plunge; so I began my locking process in November 2002.

The reasons that persuaded me to go ahead and Lock were:

- The fact that I felt I did not have control over my own hair; I felt my hair actually controlled me; dictating what and when I actually did things, such as:

    o Working out, swimming, etc.

    o Going Places or I should say not going places after doing certain activities.

    o Running for cover at the slightest moisture in the air.

- The fact that I just wanted to feel and be free from all the issues that revolve around permed hair.

    o The breakage and the tender scalp.

    o The two-week ritual of sitting in the Salon for hours on end if not all day.

WERE YOUR LOCKS STARTED BY A PROFESSIONAL AND/OR DID YOU START THEM YOURSELF OR HAVE A FRIEND HELP YOU?

A professional, and now friend, Kalimah "LocMama" Johnson, started and still continue to nurture my locks.

WHAT BENEFITS HAVE YOU GAINED FROM LOCKING YOUR HAIR?

(PHYSICAL, MENTAL, SPIRTUAL, EMOTIONAL)

- I now have a sense of freedom to express my individuality. I am no longer bound by society's idea of beauty.

- Before I locked I always felt like the real me had not yet shown through, I am now steps closer to letting my true-self shine.

- I can now exercise, swim or walk in the rain whenever I want without being concerned with the hair.

WHAT WAS THE BEST & WORST THING ANYONE EVER SAID TO YOU ABOUT YOUR LOCKS & WHO WAS IT THAT SAID IT?

BEST COMMENTS:

- Even when I was devastated after having my shoulder length hair cut to approximately two inches, my husband was extremely supportive and would continuously say how he would love me even if I were bald.

- Actually, some of my best comments were made by those of non-African decent. Complete strangers, usually Caucasians would come up to tell me how becoming my locks were and how they just seem to fit me; some would even go as far to say how they wish they could do the same with their hair.

WORST COMMENTS:

- It's actually sad to say that one of my worst comments actually came from a family member who stated "Why did you put that SHIT in your hair, don't you know that we have "GOOD HAIR"!

- Another time that totally stands out is when I first started my locking journey, I remember a long time acquaintance said "Girl you really must me going through something to do that to yourself" as she chuckled.

WHAT WOULD YOU SAY TO A BLACK WOMAN (OR ANY WOMAN) WHO IS THINKING ABOUT LOCKING HER HAIR, BUT HAS RESERVATIONS?

There is nothing wrong with taking your time and thinking about if locking is something that you truly want to do. Even though times are changing, I still think that society standard of beauty concerning hair not only by African Americans but also females in general is long silky strands. When you decide upon the journey to lock you are going against the grain and if you are not grounded in your reasons as to why you are taking the journey, I think you will have a harder time with the whole process. Especially those who lock because they think it is the latest fade or that they will have maintenance free hair! Even though the journey is not easy those who decide to take the plunge will be very enlightened in more ways then they can image. I would also advise someone considering locking to have a consultation with a loctician to answer any questions or concerns. Do not be afraid to ask the loctician about your hair texture and how it will look locked. Ask to see pictures of the locticians work. Ask questions about the locking process and ask them to tell you about their experiences. Try and connect with a loctician who will advise you on the actual care of your natural hair and eventually how to twist your own locks. Learning how to care for your own locks means you will never have a "Hair Emergency"!

Last but not least, I would advise someone to make sure they enjoy each and every stage of the locking process, because believe me, you will miss it! And last but not least I would advise one to embrace and learn from the journey!

HAVE YOU LEARNED ANY LESSONS FROM LOCKING YOUR HAIR, IF SO, WHAT?

- Locking has made me a stronger individual, confirming that I can conquer adversity and still come out on top.

- Through locking I am one step closer to not letting things said or how I am viewed by others get in my way of what I want.

- My locking experience has made me more accepting of myself as well as others.

- I think the most important part that I have learned through my journey of locking, and still learning, is the need for a supportive inner circle of individuals. I absolutely love my hair, and you will too!

Crystal-Traditional Locks

Mom/Entrepreneur/Shoe Collector

I started locking my hair in March 2002. Two years before I was disappointed in my hair. Although it was past my shoulders in length, it was no longer thick and healthy like it had been. Years of perming my hair had thinned it out and changed the texture. My hair would not even hold curls! I had to go to the salon weekly in order to have a good hair day...in my mind.

My locks were started by Kalimah Johnson. She was my first and only lock stylist and I have never had anyone else groom my locks and I pray that I will never need anyone else to do them!

The physical benefits are how beautiful I feel, I look in the mirror and I am always satisfied with my hair.

In discussing the mental benefits I have to say that first, society plays a huge role in how we see ourselves. The images that are thrown at us (that don't represent us) over and over again; can distort the mental image we have about what it beautiful. Beauty is defined as..."the quality present in a thing or person that gives intense pleasure or deep satisfaction to the mind"...paraphrased. Whether arising from sensory manifestations, (as in shape, color, sound, etc.), or a meaningful design or pattern, or something else (such as a personality in which high spiritual qualities are manifested). We tend to respond to those images that we are inundated with.

Therefore, in other words, when you can look at yourself and feel good about the way you look it won't matter about society's image of beauty. Locking your hair will change what you see as beautiful and you will begin to look at everything around you as if you are seeing it for the first time.

Locking my hair has given me ultimate Freedom. I now know Freedom from chemicals and Freedom from countless hours at the salon. I have Freedom to get my hair wet and the Freedom of more time. I have Freedom to experience all levels of beauty!

No one has ever said anything bad to me about my locks. There were those that didn't like them when they were short (my ex-husband), there were those that preferred my hair straight and there were those who just didn't understand why I would do such a thing.

The positive responses I have received far outweigh any of the doubters I have encountered. I receive wonderful compliments about my hair on a daily basis.

I would say to any woman who has been thinking about locking her hair to first think, meditate and pray about the reasons why you want to lock your hair, consider the negativity you will encounter if you decide, and pray for the strength to endure it all. It will be the best decision you ever make regarding your hair. It will totally change the way you view yourself. You will ask yourself, "What took me so long?" I encourage you to go ahead and do it. I have not regretted it!!!

From locking my hair, I have learned that all the heat, chemicals and other black hair "care" products do much more damage than good.

I have learned that our hair will grow without all of the products.

I have learned that people still view me as beautiful without straight hair.

I have learned that I am beautiful and love being happy, nappy and FREE!!!!

This is another picture of my hair with it down!

Sonya-Traditional Locks

Mom/Wife/Event Planner

I decided to lock my hair for two reasons. First, I thought they were beautiful on other people and seeing them gave me a newfound appreciation for the natural state of our hair. Second, I got tired of spending my entire Saturday in a hair salon. The split ends from relaxers just about wore me out. I was tired of how my hair would look between visits with the difference in the new growth and relaxed hair as well.

My locks were started by a professional, the "LocMama".

From locking my hair I have gained the benefit of being even more confident in who I am, getting closer to the gift of patience, and the ability to swim/work out without being worried about my hair getting messed up or not looking right afterwards.

The worst thing anyone ever said to me was when my Granny first saw my baby locks she replied, "OOOOH Sonya, you look like you got rat titties on your head". The best thing someone said to me was when my mother in law, who is a cosmetologist, finally commented after about 2 years. She said, "Sonya, at first I was uneasy about you growing locks, but now I think they are beautiful and you wear them well. Kalimah sure knows what she is doing!"

I would say to any woman who is thinking about locking her hair that "I encourage you to do it. But you must know that growing locks is a process of; change, patience, acceptance, and satisfaction. In knowing this make sure you are ready mentally to go through the stages. Once you do you will feel so free! It's exhilarating!"

I have learned that it is ok to step out on faith and to do some things that you want to do for "YOU". We should not always conform to the thoughts and stereotypes of other people. No matter what it is, when you finally do it you become an example and/or a wealth of knowledge to other people.

For instance, I have been wearing my locks the past 6 years. I have had people not only compliment my hair but ask me so many questions about it. My experience, confidence and knowledge can stump out the ignorance of others. My own husband hated the idea of me growing locks and didn't hesitate to tell me not to. But I did it anyway (for me). Some 3 years later he appreciated them so much that he grew some and so did our 8-year-old son! So go ahead girlfriend, we are out here, we support you and you will not regret it! I am sure of it.

Last but not least, this is what Joy had to say about locking her hair. For those of you who may not remember, she is the first person who introduced me to the concept of freedom and locking your hair for healing and well-being. Her words are powerful and had to be included in this book.

Joy Royes

Mother/Partner/Lawyer/Activist

I locked my hair because when I was doing my undergraduate studies I found out that the African-American community is the consumer base of the beauty products industry. I believe the statistic at the time was 60% of an 8 billion dollar per year industry. When I began to calculate what 60% of 8 billion dollars could do if it remained in our communities, I found it a little bit overwhelming that we spent that in large part to have hair that was not representative of what we were born with. I locked my hair out of frustration and hope. I locked my hair as part of my own spiritual, economic, and community affirmation.

My locks were started by a young man who is now a professional, but he was just starting out then. He had been working at a shop that did natural hair care, but I was the first customer that he ever did out of his home. He has since over the years become a bit of a natural hair care icon.

I locked my hair for myself because I wanted to say to the world that we are all beautiful just as God created us. It was an external expression of what I was feeling inside. Over the years that expression has grown and I have become increasingly adept at reading it. It now serves as an internal control on the care that I am providing for myself. The condition of my hair will shift according to changes in me. I have learned to respond to these shifts and changes and as such take better care of myself. It has been the affirmation that I hoped it would be. It has been the springboard for conversations with countless others who do not look like me and therefore pivotal in my own growth and evolution.

The worst thing anyone has ever said about my hair was to call them "extensions." Some might not find that offensive, but to me it negated the fact that I grew these and I care for them. My hair lives, breathes, and is very much a part of my living being. They did not come out of plastic and get attached. The best thing that anyone has ever said about my locks is "You make me feel like I can look good in locks."

I would say that locking your hair is a labor of love and it should best be undertaken as a journey. Of course, not all women make it that deep, but it can be and if it has that potential why not take it as deep as it can go? Your hair can teach you a lot about you. The journey of locking (if you choose for it to be a journey) can show you exactly where you stand on commitment, patience, arrogance, insecurity, and a whole host of other things but you have to be open. Also I would say lock in the summer, so you can wear hats all through the fall and by spring you will have beautiful locks without having to endure the aggravation of their "adolescent" stage.

Being a professional who chooses to lock her hair will show you exactly what you are made of. People of color have deeply held beliefs about the meaning and significance of our hair and how it defines us, but unfortunately we are not even aware of them. When you make a conscious choice to abandon all that you have known to choose a natural path, the lessons that you learn are all about you. You find out exactly what you are made of; you will discover insecurities that you never knew you had, but ultimately it provides you a unique opportunity to confront, face, and fix that mess. Natural hair provides the same freedom that nature in general does! Embrace freedom.

More pictures of women who have locked their hair:

Kalimah Johnson

As Is…

Lock Lovin'

I'm lovin' your locks

The way they move and sway

Moving negatives out of your way

Your locks are upon your head like a jeweled crown

For queens who have seen the best and the worst of it all

Angelic, Heroic, Strong, Soft and everything serene

Lock Lovin'

Holding above them

Glowing and Growing

Signifying Naps

Needing the kink to make me think about me

About you, about true

Lock Lovin'

Proud and Loud

Wherever you go

He Knows

She Knows

That your Locks are the new Perm

Kalimah Johnson

Jiggaboo Jazzy

Nice and Nappy

Medusa Diva

Lockmama

Twisted Sister

Buckshot Hot

Locked up

Whether they like it or not

Frizzy Fuzzy Fly

As is…

Lock loving above it

As is…

Honoring

Isis Goddess

Nefertitti Queen

Candace Queen

Cleopatra Queen and

Mother of all Life-She be black-but they keep calling her "Lucy"

Lock Lovin'

As Is…

Lock Lovin'

Common Language

There is a need for a common language among natural hair care specialists, wearers and consumers alike, as evidenced by the responses from women who have made the connection as well as the many terms I have used throughout this book. With that being said, here is a call out to all natural hair care specialists, wearers, lovers of nappy hair to go to my website and send me any comments, terminology, language and proper usage so that we can compile a natural hair care dictionary for us, by us. I hope to hear from you soon! Go to www.myspace.com/PicNap and click on the mail tab and send me a message.

Tools for Traditional/Salon Locks

Barbers Comb

Towel

Water Based Gel

Light Oil

Scissors

Metal Clips (Long and Short)

Water Bottle

Parting Comb

Cape

Please see Chapter 3 for further detail.

Lock Etiquette

Here are ten basic rules you should go by to be on the safe side of not offending someone who wears locks. This list is not intended to be extensive; it is more of a guideline with flexible principles depending on the lock wearer. These are just suggestions that were developed as a result of listening to clients talk and asking them specifically what peeves them about others who encounter their locks and the things they say and do around them.

1. Do not refer to locks as "those things in your hair" or "braids."

2. Do not touch a persons locks unless you have permission to do so.

3. Do not ask if they wash them...of course they do.

4. Do not say, "That looks good on you but I could never..."

5. Do not ask, "When are you going to wear your real hair?"

6. Do not assume that the lock wearer smokes marijuana.

7. Do not assume that the lock wearer ascribes to a particular religion or lifestyle.

8. Do learn more about locks of the lock wearer by asking open-ended questions.

9. Do your own research about locking before making comments + or –.

10. Do respect "all kinds of locks" by honoring those who wear them, i.e. treat people the way you would like to be treated.

Epiphany Page

Here is a picture of me now! My locks are now more than five years old. The best thing anyone ever said to me about my locks was, "It took you so *long* to lock your hair, now *this* is how you are *supposed* to look." The worst thing was, "God *don't* make mistakes honey, but I think *you did* by wearing your hair like that!" I got over it quickly because the benefits I have reaped from wearing my hair in locks outweighed her comment. I believe that if you are in search of some healing in your life and if you are tired of the standards that have been placed on you in this country for so long...lock your hair! It will give you answers to questions you did not even know you had! I am glad I locked my hair and wrote this book for those of you who are thinking about it, but just too afraid to take the leap. I also know that wearing your hair in it's natural state is just as liberating! However, I am partial to locks because there is something a little different about the experience than wearing it in an afro or braided or anything else that our hair can do. It is a lesson in patience, tolerance, loving yourself and so many other things that I cannot begin to explain to you. I have considered cutting my locks off so when you see me at a signing and the locks are gone, don't be surprised! I have allowed my locks to go through all the phases and have considered going back to an afro. It is something you will have to find out for yourself. I love you because you are a part of this universe, now go out there and be beautiful in it!

As is…

Bibliography

No Lye: The African American Woman's Guide to Natural Hair Care by *Tulani Kinard*

Braiding: Easy Styles for Everyone (Personal Care Collection) by *Jones*

Let's Talk Hair: Every Black Woman's Personal Consultation for Healthy Growing Hair by *Pamela Ferrell*

Hairlocking: Everything You Need to Know: African, Dread and Nubian Locks by *Nekhena Evans*

Hair Rules! : The Ultimate Hair-Care Guide for Women with Kinky, Curly, or Wavy Hair by *Anthony Dickey*

The American Heritage Dictionary: Second College Edition by *Houghton Mifflin Company*

Social Work Treatment: Fourth Edition by Turner, Free Press

Techniques and Guidelines for Social Work Practice: Third Edition by Sheafor and Horejsi

WEB DIRECTORY

www.PicNap.com

www.myspace.com/PicNap

www.myspace.com/picnappoetrypage

www.lockstylist.com

www.everettes-cornrows.com

www.locks4life.com

About the Author

Kalimah Johnson is the proud owner of PicNap™ Natural Hair Care Artistry. She has cultivated and refined her expertise in natural hairstyles since the 1970's. As a Master Loctician with several years of experience, her personal mission is to create a healthy black consciousness within her community. Her adoration for natural hair and her dedication to providing detailed attention to her clients has won her praise from the industry, but most importantly from her loyal client base. It is this commitment that has encouraged her to create a new exclusive line of services and merchandise called PicNap™. Through the launch of Picnap™ Kalimah produces natural hair care events and workshops, as well as produce and host one of the hottest open mic venues in the mid-west. Kalimah Johnson holds a Master's Degree in Social Work, and is a published performance poet. Her skills and talent have allowed her to incorporate group processing when Conducting Picnap™ gatherings. The events have allowed her clients the opportunity to dialogue about the negative social repercussions and connotations of nappy hair. They have also provided her clients with a forum to embrace the hidden potential of nappy hair. She is dedicated to nurturing pride in black people, and removing the myths and challenges related to hair locking. Her creative blend of poetry and performance is used to entertain, inform and celebrate the topic of natural black hair. She has established herself as a unique and gifted Natural Hair Care Artist/Master Loctician with a knack for bringing out the very best in her clients. Go To: www.picnap.com to hear and purchase her spoken word projects. Downtown Detroit, MI Phone: (313) 606-2342 Email: Ebani@hotmail.com

NOTES PAGE

2172115

Made in the USA